The Magic of Basketball

This book belongs to:

_____

Basketball is the magical gift that keeps on giving,
From a young age to old, the gifts are everlasting.

v

Published by: Kayla Alexander

ISBN-13: 978-1-9992095-0-6

This book is dedicated to my parents and sister. Thank you for believing in me, encouraging all my ideas and always pushing me to dream big. It is dedicated to the game of basketball. This game has blessed me in ways I never could have imagined.

Lastly, this book is dedicated to you the reader. Dare to dream big and then follow it up with hard work. You'll be amazed at where life takes you!

— Kayla Alexander

Kayla was 12 years old when she first learned to play basketball.
She would soon discover that basketball had magical gifts to give to all.

Basketball is the magical gift that keeps on giving,
From a young age to old, the gifts are everlasting.

Gift number one came before her introduction to the sport:
The lifelong friend who first put her on a court.

Hi my name is Nikki, and you are tall like me.
Come to a basketball tryout, it will be fun you'll see!

During the tryout it was clear Kayla was just a beginner.
But the coach could see with her height she could be made into a winner.

Your height is a gift that no coach can teach,
But learning basketball is a goal anyone can reach!

Gift number two was a lesson she would never overlook.
Basketball taught her the importance of practice and hard work.

It will take hours of repetition if I want to make it all the way.
But in the pursuit of greatness that's a small price to pay.

Kayla struggled to dribble the ball, complete a pass or make a shot.
But she was eager to learn and practiced everything she was taught.

One dribble, two dribbles, three dribbles, four,
One step, two steps, in the basket, score!

Gift number three was the confidence growing from within.
She went from shy to assertive, a trait needed to win.

Stance, bend my knees, and follow through with my wrist.
These foul shots will tie the game, and I know I won't miss!

Kayla was once unsure and would speak with reservation,
But basketball is a sport that requires a lot of communication.

"Shot!" Her teammates call, "grab the rebound!"
"Loose ball" Kayla yells as she dives to the ground!

Gift number four was the importance of teamwork for success.
The team had twelve players and they couldn't succeed with any less.

I rebound, Sarah shoots, Keshia sets up the play.
We need everyone's abilities to make it all the way.

Kayla's team extended beyond the twelve players on the court.
She had family and friends who were always there to support.

Turning weaknesses into strengths comes with a lot of sweat and tears.
But I have amazing people in my life who have helped me over the years.

Gift number five was receiving a college education for free. She was given a scholarship to play basketball at Syracuse University.

College Signing Day!

My mother and father are so proud of me.
I get to play basketball while I earn my degree.

Kayla was a student athlete, which meant schoolwork needed to be done.
This required balancing classes and homework with basketball fun.

Early morning practice followed by classes I must attend.
I know that this busy schedule will be worth it in the end.

Gift number six was an important lesson in time management.
Kayla used an agenda to make sure her time was well spent.

I have no time to go see a movie today.
I have an assignment that is due on Friday.

After 4 years of sacrifice and dedication, Kayla left it all on the floor.
She was the first player to reach 2000 points, finishing with a total of 2024.

I never shot a three, only layups, jump shots and hooks.
But I scored enough baskets to go down in my school's history books!

Gift number seven was the ability to have a career playing basketball. Kayla was drafted by the San Antonio Stars with the 8th pick overall.

Paid to play basketball, this is what I love to do.
Wow I can't believe it, this is a dream come true!

Kayla's first summer playing in the WNBA would prove to be quite hard.
The game was faster, the players bigger, stronger and more difficult to guard.

Sylvia Fowles and Jayne Appel, they're much stronger than me.
I'm playing against athletes I used to watch on TV!

Gift number eight was learning that perseverance would be key.
Kayla worked through the struggles to get the results she wanted to see.

Film room, extra reps and lots of cardio.
In no time at all I will be playing like a pro.

Kayla realized that she could contribute to the team even if she didn't play.
It was three years before she earned a starting spot on game day.

It took patience, persistence and being a good teammate.
But seeing my playing time increase was worth the work and wait.

Gift number nine was being able to **travel** worldwide,
Playing on many teams and representing Canada with pride.

In every new country and city, I make sure to take in every sight.
A job playing basketball and travelling has been an absolute delight.

Kayla was able to travel through America while playing in the summer
And then go overseas in the winter, which was never a bummer.

Russia, France and South Korea, traveling east and west,
But playing in Australia was an experience above the rest.

Gift number ten was growing into an important leadership role.
Passing down the lessons basketball taught her was the main goal.

HAVE CONFIDENCE!

DREAM BIG!

WORK HARD!

PERSEVERE!

BE A LEADER!

BUILD FRIENDSHIPS!

I share many of my lessons if you take a close look.
It's one of the reasons I decided to write you this book.

Kayla continues to play the sport with the same joy as when she was small. To think all of these magical gifts came through the game of basketball.

Gift One - Friendship

Gift Two - Hard Work

Gift Three - Confidence

Gift Four - Teamwork

Gift Five- Education

Gift Six- Time Management

Gift Seven- Career

Gift Eight- Perseverance

Gift Nine- Travel

Gift Ten- Leadership

Basketball is the magical gift that keeps on giving,
From a young age to old, the gifts are everlasting.

Follow your dreams and work hard without hesitation,
When you believe in yourself there is no limitation.

Basketball gave Kayla 10 gifts and a dream come true.
What magical gifts can your dreams give to you?

MY DREAMS:

What are your dreams? Write them all down so you don't forget!

MY GOALS:

Goals are the actions you take to make your dreams come true.
What are some actions or steps you can start taking today
to help you achieve some of your dreams?

About the Authors:

The character of "Kayla" is based on co-author Kayla Alexander's real life experiences. Kayla has been playing basketball professionally for seven years. Before she was introduced to the sport, her first love was art. To this day she can spend hours drawing and illustrating in her free time. When she is not playing basketball or drawing, she loves speaking to and working with kids; inspiring them to dream big and work fearlessly towards accomplishing those dreams. You can learn more about Kayla at www.kaylaalexander.net.

Kayla & Kesia

Kesia is an avid basketball fan and president of the "Kayla Alexander Fan Club". While she has never played at the collegiate or professional level, she still maintains that she taught Kayla everything she knows. Before molding Kayla into the player she is today, Kesia was an Ontario scholar with a very average high school basketball career. When she is not obsessing over both of her siblings' basketball success, she enjoys reading, staying active and writing the occasional witty Instagram caption. Kesia currently works in Human Resources.

Basketball is the magical gift that keeps on giving,
From a young age to old, the gifts are everlasting.

Made in United States
Orlando, FL
11 October 2022

23257721R00024